101
USES FOR THE
UNEMPLOYED

101
USES FOR THE
UNEMPLOYED

NEUMAN & NEUMAN

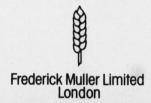

Frederick Muller Limited
London

First published in Great Britain in 1983 by
Frederick Muller Limited, Dataday House,
Alexandra Road, London SW19 7JZ

Reprinted 1984

Published in the United States of America by
Pinnacle Books Inc., 1430 Broadway, New York 10018

British Library Cataloguing in Publication Data

Neuman, Virginia F.
  101 uses for the unemployed.
  1. Unemployed—Great Britain
  I. Title   II. Neuman, Paul Glen
  331.13'7941   HD5765
  ISBN 0–584–11076–6

Printed in Great Britain by
Redwood Burn Limited, Trowbridge, Wilts
and Bound by Pegasus Bookbinding, Melksham, Wilts

Dedication:
TO ANYONE LOOKING FOR A JOB

101
USES FOR THE
UNEMPLOYED

J. Newman

J. Neuman

J. Newman

PARK IN REAR

V. Newman

V. Neuman.

J. Neumann

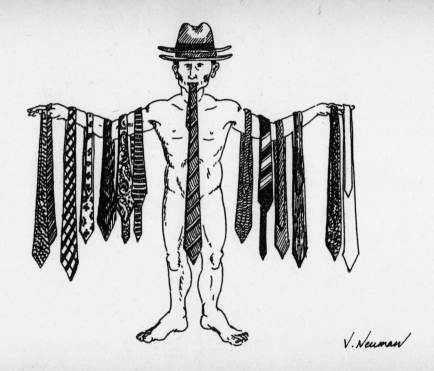

J. Neuman

J. Newman.

J. Neuman.

J. Neumann

J. Neuman

J. Neuman.

PEOPLE'S
CHOICE
DOG FOOD

YUM
YUM
YUMMY!

100% HUMA

PE
C
DO

J. Newman.

V. Neuman.

J. Neuman

J. Neuman.

V. Newman

J. Neuman.

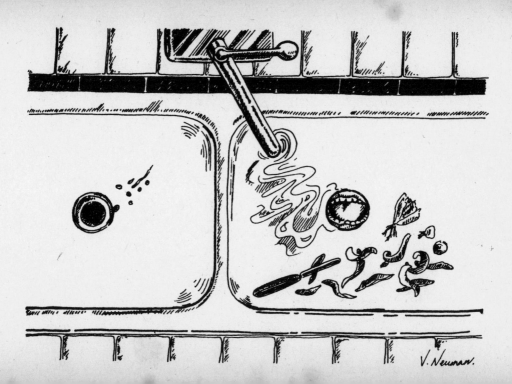

V. Neuman.

V. Neuman

J. Neuman.

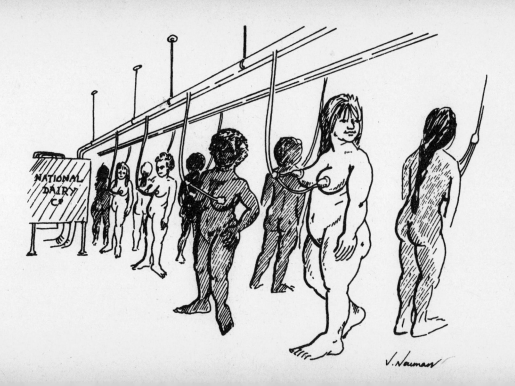

J. Neuman

J. Neuman.

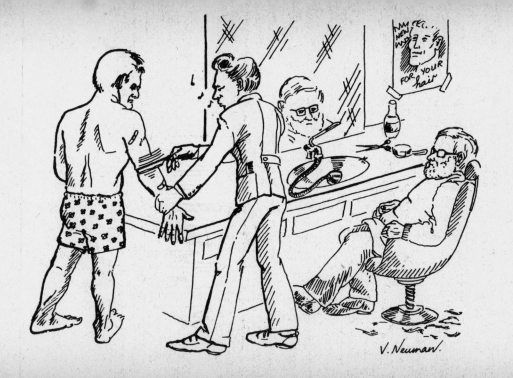

V. Neuman.

J. Neuman

ENTRANCE

J. Neuman

J. Neumann

V. Neuman

V. Neuman.

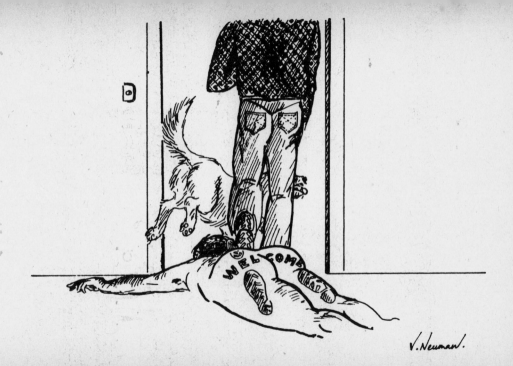

V. Newman.

J. Neuman.

J. Nauman

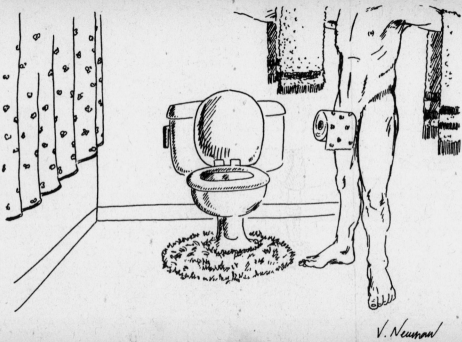

V. Neuman